Who knows best?

Mikey and other poems

STEPHEN WILDBLOOD

Illustrated by Andrew Prescott

First published 2022

Published under licence by Brown Dog Books and
The Self-Publishing Partnership Ltd,
10b Greenway Farm, Bath Rd, Wick, nr. Bath BS30 5RL

ISBN printed book: 978-1-83952-536-0

Written by Stephen Wildblood

Cover, internal design and illustrations by Andrew Prescott

Printed and bound in the UK

This book is printed on FSC certified paper

For Annie, Esther and Rafa

Table of Contents

Mikey 9
The Punk Dragon 15
The Toad 21
The Troll 27
Rufus the Pirate 33
Little Red Riding Hood (RIP) 37

Mikey

This is the dog, Mikey, who saved the whole world,
and this is the wood where his story unfurled.

Here is the stream shimmering down to the sea
and this is the fish with the eyes that could see
terrible Bert, in his terrible digger
counting his money from making towns bigger.

Mikey was out strolling, he stood on a log,
admiring some petals and kissing a frog.
The fish watched him closely, he wasn't quite sure,
if kissing a frog wasn't breaking the law.

The stream bubbled clear and refreshingly cool,
but rainbow trout Trevor was nobody's fool.
He knew what men did when they dug up the land
to put up more houses as cities expand.

He knew dirty water and smells with no frills
and hated the muck that got caught in his gills.
He heard the loud noise as the digger began
and trembled with fear as it just missed a lamb.

It rammed down an ash with an ear-splitting roar,
a branch as it fell hit Mikey's left paw.
The fish leapt up high as he heard the dog yelp
and said, 'Come over here, this water will help.'

Mikey bathed his paw as the fish carried on,
'If they cut down this wood, this stream will be gone.
Our old home will then disappear without trace,
this beauty and peace they will never replace.

You see the pipes there which are stacked in that pile,
they'll carry this water for over a mile
to huge man-made tanks made of red man-made stones
to store up our water for new man-made homes.

Then fishes will perish and flowers will die
but worse is to come,' said the fish with a sigh.
'For under that stream is a monster that's wild,
the sort that would terrify any young child.

Its long arms are spotty, its tummy bright blue,
its five eyes are gungy, its nose dribbles too.
It's called The Old Stinkslug, and rightfully so,
it's not had a wash for a century or so.

It lives in a cave that is under the stream
and if it's disturbed it will run out and scream.
The world will be full of its odious stink
and mountains will crumble and countries will sink.

On some dark foggy nights it crawls through the town
and leaves a long trail that is slimy and brown.
But if a child's window is left on the latch
it opens it up to see what it can catch.

It leans through the window and waves its black claw
which silently closes the child's bedroom door.
Then reaching across and approaching the bed
it thinks about gobbling a child up instead.

Then only the stench of the town's rubbish heap
will make it decide to leave children asleep
and slither away for its favourite meal
of rotting old waste mixed with slimy old peel.

And after its guzzled its tummy will ache
and rumble so much it could make the earth quake.
It's this magic water that dampens its pain
and stops it from stinking and screaming again.

The stream must keep flowing, the world must not die.
We all need your help, Mikey, please can you try?
The man must stop digging and leave us alone,
they don't need new houses, this wood is our home.'

So Mikey decided to give out a growl
and look at bad Bert with his most fearsome scowl.
But that plan was useless, the horrid man said
'buzz off, little doggie, go home to your bed'.

Mikey went home but then crept out at night
when the silver moon shone and stars twinkled bright.
He let out a howl that was wailing and loud,
the type that would make even fiercest wolves proud.

He howled and he howled keeping children awake,
from midnight to dawn, when he saw the day break.
And next night he went there and howled once again,
chilling the dark night with his fearful refrain.

The third night he howled on the top of a hill,
his silhouette looked like a wolf out to kill.
The people were frightened and said to bad Bert
'Forget building there, before someone gets hurt.

We won't buy your houses, we'll stay where we are.
We think we'd prefer now to buy a new car
and leave that old forest with air crystal clear
so maybe that mean wolf will then disappear.'

So Bert stopped his digging, deciding instead
to grow swedes and turnips and live in a shed.
Mikey and Trevor have said never a word
and as to Old Stinkslug, no more has been heard.

He lives in his cave but consumes all the mess,
created by people who could not care less.
And Mikey is happy and never does boast,
he's stopped kissing frogs, liking flowers the most.

Now over the proud oaks the birds sing and cry
'Look after our woods so the world does not die'.
Trevor and Mikey still play chase in the pool
and the magical stream runs clear, bright and cool.

The Punk Dragon

Cedric the punk dragon was fed up and cold.
His flame had gone out and his cave smelt of mould.
No fire would come out when he gave a big puff
Just sweet-smelling breath and a load of old guff.

Cedric's old mother was called Doris by name.
She'd boxed at Olympics but now was quite lame.
She came from East London and knew Cockney slang
A bruiser, a mobster and queen of her gang.

She spoilt her son rotten and called him 'Big Rick'
and boiled him up carrots, which just made him sick.
He said 'Mum, forget it. I'm now a big bloke
I'm not eating carrots, for flames I need coke.'

They flew to a wizard, quite new in the trade,
Who dabbled in heating and magical aid.
He had no real clue how to do a true spell.
The best he could make was a very bad smell.

The wizard told Ricky, 'I'll give you a cure.
You must eat this garlic, it's costly but pure.
I dug it in moonlight whilst casting a spell
Then mixed it with dew drops to dampen the smell.'

'Whatever!' said Doris. 'You do talk such tosh
All that you want, mate, is a load of our dosh.
I've seen you buy garlic from just up the road.
The greengrocer sells it, you lying old toad.'

The wizard said, 'Granny now don't flip your lid
For this magic potion I want fifty quid.'
'Matey,' replied Doris, 'you are 'aving a giraffe,
All that I'll pay yer is a pound and a 'alf.'

'Give me a fiver, you miserable old bird.
The price that you're paying is simply absurd.'
The wizard was brave but it was a mistake
'I'll fry you,' said Doris, 'You oily old fake.'

'Chill out Mum,' said Ricky, 'We'll give it a whirl.'
'He's right,' said the wizard 'relax my old girl.'
So Doris agreed and they flew to their cave
but stopped on the way to dance punk at a rave.

When Doris said, 'Ricky, it's medicine time.'
He stared at the potion which looked like green slime.
But holding his nose tight, he took some big slurps
yet all it produced was magnificent burps.

'That cheating old Wizard,' said Doris now mad,
'I will crunch up his bones, that rotten old cad.'
Then, to rebel Rick, 'I'll sound like a parrot
To get your flame back just eat up this carrot.'

But Ricky, said 'No, it ain't cool for a punk.'
They flew to the wizard, 'That potion was junk
You cheating old geezer, I'll boil up your 'ead
And serve it,' said Doris 'as breakfast in bed.'

'Would madam prefer our superior range?
I'm sure our best products will make such a change
To madam's dear Ricky, the darling wee chap,
Come here, little dragon, come here on my lap.

Here's some yummy tonic, I brewed it today.
From chilli and carrots I bought in Bombay.
I went there on Sunday on this magic rug.
It lights up one's fire and it kills any bug.

It comes rather pricey', the wizard went on
'but worth every penny to save your dear son.'
Then taking a sample from under his coat
He rammed a big spoonful down poor Ricky's throat.

Doris was livid: 'You have so cooked your goose
Me and my gangsters will 'ang you in a noose.
Thieving old tea leaf! Them carrots is Mabel's
Use by tomorrow is stamped on them labels.'

But Ricky ignored them and, licking his lips,
Said to himself quietly, 'That man's had his chips
But mumsie was right, these carrots are so yummy.'
And then a great belch came WHOOSH from his tummy.

He opened his mouth and let out a big shot
Of fiery flames that were sizzling and hot.
And giving a huge blast of furnace-like air
He saw that the wizard was no longer there.

'Where's that blooming wizard? I'm sick of his games.'
Asked Doris till she saw he'd gone up in flames.
'My darling wee Ricky, you're such a big hunk.
Now put all his cinders dear in this 'ere trunk.'

Cedric the punk dragon was happy and warm,
His flame had come back, he was now on top form
And Doris his mother did nothing but sing
And smoke cigarettes and get dressed up in bling.

So, D and C Heating, flashed in neon lights.
'We kill off fake wizards and most pests and mites.
Our magical potion comes straight from Bombay
We will sell it half price, but just for today.'

D+C
HEATING

The Toad

Napoleon the toad was not very bright
And like his wife, Fifi, could not get things right.
They lived in a ditch where the water just stank
And neither toad washed, so their smell was quite rank.

Their four oldest kids were as bad as their dad,
They were idle and miserable, complaining and sad.
They spent all their days just watching the telly
And were, like their dad, exceedingly smelly.

Their fifth child, called Thomas, was not like the rest
Though most of the family just thought him a pest.
He said to his dad one day, 'Are you sure
That the whole of the world is a terrible bore?'

'Now listen, my boy, I'm a reasonable bloke,
but you must understand, this world is no joke.
And people,' Dad said, 'drive me right up the pole.
Sometimes for lunch, they eat toads in the hole.

They get toads in their throats and sit on toadstools
Use green slime called soap, play leap toad at schools.
And witches,' said Dad, 'are the worst of the bunch.
They boil us in cauldrons and serve us for lunch.'

Not far from their ditch, was a young witch called Jess
Whose house was all wonky, her clothes were a mess.
Her spell book was big and incredibly long
But each time she used it the spell would go wrong.

She had all the gear, there was no doubting that,
The flowing black dress and the meowing black cat,
The black and white wand and the black pointed hat.
But she could not use them, so what use was that?

Thomas hopped round to her garden one day
As the witch tried a spell to make gold out of hay.
She mixed up some powder and hay with her broom.
But, lighting the cauldron, the whole thing went BOOM.

She caught sight of Tom when the smoke blew away
And said, 'Hello toad, can I ask you to stay?'
'Not blooming likely,' replied Tom with a hunch
'You just want to eat me as a toad on toast lunch.'

The witch replied quickly, 'You're having a laugh
I have been veggie since aged six and a half.
All of my spells are most pure and organic
My dear handsome toad, there is no need to panic.

Perhaps if you stayed you could help with this spell,
Once Tiddles the cat comes back out of the well.
This wand cost a fortune and so did the pot,
If they do not work soon, I'm dumping the lot.'

'You need to talk French,' replied Thomas, by chance
Having read on the wand 'fabriqué en France'.
The witch replied slowly 'are you sure it says that?'
As she tripped on the cauldron and blamed her black cat.

Said Thomas, remembering good manners from classes
'I'm not being rude, but don't you need glasses?'
'I'm sure that I don't, my eyesight's fantastic,'
The witch said, as she chewed some knicker elastic.

'This spaghetti is tough,' said the witch with a frown.
'I'll complain to the shop when I go into town.'
Thomas said bravely, 'Next door's an optician
I think he might help you to be a magician.

His name is Claude, he comes from Marseille.
He does discount for witches, so you'll be OK.'
Tom wanted to help but then watched with alarm
As the witch stuck her fork in the back of her arm.

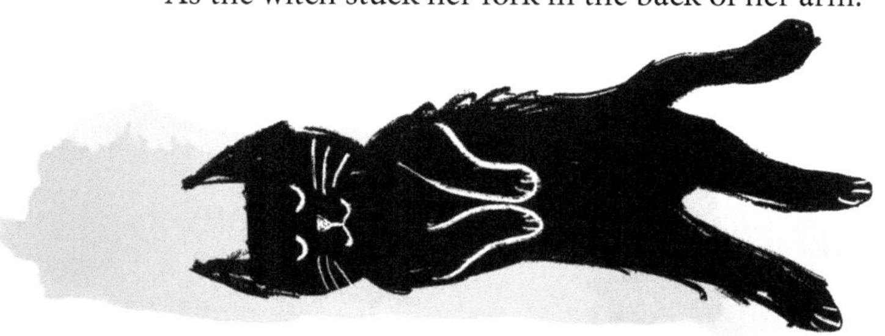

A month or so later young Thomas hopped round
And what a remarkable difference he found.
There was the witch, with gold specs on her nose,
And jewels on her fingers and rings on her toes.

The witch said, 'Hi Thomas, you'll think me a mug
But to prove that I'm not, hop onto this rug.
I've doused it with magic that I read from my book.
I can read! Yes, read! No more gobbledygook.

Claude will come with us, his work did the trick
And seeing my new riches he's married me quick.
You don't need a passport, we fly where we choose.
Life is fantastic and so are the views.

Let's go off to France – Claude's taught me the lingo
And says that in Paris they play a mean Bingo.
We'll take in a show and then eat a quick crust
Before flying on south, Monte Carlo or bust.

So Thomas went with them and week after week
He saw the world's oceans and climbed every peak.
He flew over jungles and swam in the lakes
And camped in the arctic and chatted to sheikhs.

Wherever they went he wrote letters to Dad,
'I'm having a ball, the world ain't so bad.'
Napoleon would groan and scratching his belly,
Would give a big yawn and croak, 'Switch on the telly.

Our little lad Tom is a pain in the neck
I never did manage to keep him in check.'
Then giving his tummy another good itch,
Said, 'Why didn't he stay, in this nice smelly ditch?'

The Troll

The troll under the bridge was really most polite
The problem was the goats, who loved to pick a fight.
When the troll was watching telly, all snuggled down in bed,
The goats went trip, trap, trip right above his head.

The goats lived in a field where the grass was green and lush
They chewed it and they chomped it and were never in a rush.
But though they lived in luxury, they were never satisfied,
And moaned 'the grass is so much greener on the river's other side'.

The poor troll loved the ballet and also rock and roll
And sometimes sweetest operas would sing out to his soul.
But one thing he insisted was tunes should have a beat
And so was driven mad by the sound of mistimed feet.

'It isn't trip trap trip,' he muttered to himself
As he put the metronome back on the kitchen shelf.
'It's trip trap, trip trap, trip trap, I wish those goats could see
There is a rhythm to the world, which they could learn from me.'

The troll taught that rhythm while conducting the trolls' choir.
On Sundays they'd raise the roof and practise for an hour,
The troll sang as a tenor and lots of trolls sang bass
But alto and soprano trolls were rare as pigs in space.

The troll thought of his choir one day whilst sitting in a tree
When much to his surprise there rose the sweetest melody
And looking down beneath, saw a young fox and a stoat
who were practising some descants and were hitting every note.

The troll quickly knew he had the answer to his prayer
If the fox and stoat joined them, the choir would fill the air.
So he pondered long and hard about the thing to do,
Then sent them an invite to the choir's next barbecue.

Next day the troll was watching the boring daily news
And slowly drifted off into a cosy midday snooze,
He dreamt that he was dancing to thunderous applause
The audience was on their feet and calling for encores.

Then suddenly he awoke and, while slowly coming to,
He saw he wasn't wearing a balletic pink tutu.
Just teddy bear pyjamas and slippers on his feet
And listening to the sound of a pesky goaty bleat.

Then once again he heard it, whilst munching from the fridge
And there was Little Billy Goat Gruff, trip trapping on the bridge
So up jumped the troll and said to little Billy,
'Don't you think the noise you make is really rather silly?'

'Take a leap,' said Little Billy, by way of rude reply
If you dare to pester me once more I'll punch you in the eye
I'm going to cross that bridge right now and eat that grass so green.
Where did you get that ugly face? It's really so obscene.'

Oh dear Little Billy, it is simply most unwise
To be cheeky to a big fat troll before his very eyes.
Five minutes later the troll had placed with ease
lots of tasty Billy Goat meat within his tall deep freeze.

Too late Mrs Billy Goat Gruff came rushing to the scene
She would only venture out when dressed up like the queen.
'You nasty, nasty troll,' she said, 'where is my Billykins?
If you've been mean to him, you know, I'll kick you in the shins.'

The troll's deep freeze was very tall, its drawers were very wide
And soon the next drawer down held another goat inside.
On top of the deep freeze the troll placed her tiara
And licking his lips, wished her well in the hereafter.

Next upon the bridge trip trapped Daddy Billy Goat Gruff
His beard was long, his smell was strong, he thought himself tough.
But also all about him there was lots of tasty meat
That soon was in the troll's deep freeze and made it look quite neat.

And so the troll invited round the Sunday morning choir
To join the foxes and the stoats around a barbecue fire.
He served up some salad, which was not the greatest hit,
But also lots of goats' best meat, cooked on a nice hot spit.

And after they had eaten, the animals gathered round
And soon there soared into the air a harmonious choral sound.
The trolls sang the low notes whilst others sang up high,
And with sweet song after song they filled the evening sky.

As he listened to the choir the troll was filled with joy
It took him back to days when he had been a very happy boy.
And soon the choir was known throughout the songful shire,
in memory of the goats, as the Von Tripp Trapp Family Choir.

Rufus the Pirate

Red Rufus the rapper, a pirate and stud,
Disliked hurting people or spilling their blood.
If ever he heard 'ahoy there, me hearty'
He'd wave a white flag and hold a wild party.

He'd done loads of buckling and plenty of swash.
And stolen the money of folks that are posh.
He hid chests of jewels as he sailed ocean waves
But X marks the spot now of next week's wild raves.

He bopped like a legend and knew how to chat
His ripped jeans were trendy as was his straw hat.
He cleared the streets yelling, 'Double the measure.
The booze is on me. Let's spend all that treasure.'

Though Cuthbert the Cutlass thought fighting was cool,
If he hit the dance floor he looked like a fool.
His moves were all clumsy, he grooved like a tramp
When faced with the salsa all he did was stamp.

He jived like a monkey, he wrecked the cha cha
But when someone laughed 'now show us your Rumba',
He whisked out his cutlass, waved it round his head
And said 'don't diss me mate, or else you'll be dead'.

Rufus watched Cuthbert and felt very sad
'That boy is just lonely he ain't quite that bad.
Come dance with me Cuthbert. I'll teach you some moves.
Just open your mind up and get in the grooves.'

Then Rufus said, 'Cuthbert, you're now my best friend.
Let's be civil partners till both our lives end.'
The moral of this tale, be you girl or chap,
Is stick with your partner and don't mind their rap.

Little Red Riding Hood (RIP)

Red Riding Hood, called Curly, a rude and spoiled brat.
Said 'Mum you never listen, I want a brand new hat.
I want ribbons for my curls. I want some shiny shoes.
You'd better get them quickly, or you'll be next week's news.'

She knew the wolf was watching and teased him with her chants
As she went into the woods and kicked down flowers and plants.
'That wolf should use some perfume, I cannot bear his stink.
Shall I wear my wolf skin coat or maybe stick to mink?'

Wolves are now endangered because people shoot them dead,
Moaning they have eerie howls, then pumping them with lead.
But their sad calls are nothing, they cry in fear and doubt,
To Red Riding Hood's long whinge and ever-present pout.

The wolf was really patient, a lovely handsome chap
But patience has its limits and this girl made him SNAP.
So racing round to granny's and trying not to gag
He gobbled up her granny, a wretched gristly hag.

Then waiting in her bed and feeling somewhat peckish
He put on granny's clothes and licked his lips with relish.
When Curly came inside, with her finger up her nose,
She knew it was the wolf, she could see his great big toes.

'Your teeth are too big,' she said 'what stupid, saggy eyes.
I think those hairy ears should be labelled XL size.
What do you think you're doing in granny's best night-gear?
You stink like Daddy's breath after too much home brewed beer.'

Then wolf did us a favour and ate the ghastly creep
With gran, the hag, as first course he then fell fast asleep.
But deep inside his tummy he heard the small girl shout,
'I'm going to tell my Mummy so you just let me out!'

Soon arrived the huntsman who ignored her bitter cries.
He knew all about her and was tired of her lies.
'Hurt the wolf to let you out? Are you out of your mind?
That's what you deserve, my girl, for being so unkind.'

The moral of this story rests with the wolf, you see,
'If you're a spoilt brat never, ever, mess with me.'

BURP!